# Key Stage 2

# Vocabulary

## Carol Matchett

Name _____

Schofield & Sims

The English language is amazing: there are so many words to choose from. The more words you know, the easier it is for you to read and understand books and write your ideas effectively.

This book will help you to develop your word power by encouraging you to take an interest in words. It shows you how to understand words and how to choose the best words when writing. The examples will help you to see why understanding words is important, and the activities will introduce you to words and give you practice in using them.

## Finding your way around this book

Before you start using this book, write your name in the name box on the first page. Then decide how to begin. If you want a complete course on improving your vocabulary, you should work right through the book from beginning to end.

Another way to use the book is to dip into it when you want to find out about a particular topic, such as homographs. The Contents page will help you to find the pages you need. Whichever way you choose, don't try to do too much at once – it's better to work through the book in short bursts.

When you have found the topic you want to study, look out for these icons, which mark different parts of the text.

### Activities

This icon shows you the activities that you should complete. You write your answers in the spaces provided. After you have worked through all the activities on the page, turn to pages 39 to 48 to check your answers. When you are sure that you understand the topic, add a tick in the box beside it on the Contents page.

On page 38 you will find suggestions for some projects (**Now you try**), which will give you even more opportunities to improve your vocabulary.

### Explanation

This text explains the topic and gives examples. Make sure you read it before you start the activities.

This text gives you useful background information about the subject.

# Contents

## Explanation

Good readers and writers have **word power**. They know and understand lots of words and they know when and how to use them.

When you are reading or listening you will often come across **new words** that you have not heard or seen before. Don't just ignore them! Discovering new words is a great opportunity to improve your word power. Instead, try asking yourself **what the word means**. Once you know what a word means it will be stored in your word memory so that you can use it in the future.

## Activities

**1** Here are some words that you might come across when reading. Do you know what they mean? **Write the meaning** of as many of the words as you can.

Don't worry if you don't know all these word meanings. That's what this book is all about …

|   | Word | Meaning |
|---|------|---------|
| a | frail | |
| b | vain | |
| c | billow | |
| d | plunge | |
| e | weary | |
| f | commence | |
| g | location | |
| h | isolated | |
| i | adequate | |

## Did you know?

No-one knows for sure how many words there are in the English language. It is impossible to count them because more and more new words are always being invented.

# Understanding word meanings 2

## Explanation

Quite often you can **infer**, or work out, what a word means from the way it is used in a sentence.

**Example** This train **terminates** at the next station. Will all passengers please get ready to leave the train?

From reading the rest of the sentence you can guess that the word 'terminates' means 'comes to an end'.

## Activities

**1** Read these sentences and try to **infer**, or work out, the **meaning** of the word in **bold**. Underline the word in the box that gives the closest meaning.

a The house made out of bricks was good and **sturdy**.

| plain | strong | small | weak |
|---|---|---|---|

b We gasped at the table that was piled high with all sorts of **delectable** food.

| smelly | horrid | cold | tasty |
|---|---|---|---|

c The team were **eliminated from** the competition when they lost in the third round.

knocked out of      added to

moved from      started      disqualified

d The sails on the windmill began to **rotate**.

fall off      fly away

stand still      go round

e Luckily the police were able to **thwart** the robber's getaway.

| help | miss | whack | stop |
|---|---|---|---|

f It was not the *real* FA Cup. It was just a **replica**.

| picture | copy | design | surprise |
|---|---|---|---|

g The ice on the roads made them **treacherous**.

| uneven | safe | dangerous | expensive |
|---|---|---|---|

# Using a dictionary

If you are not sure about a word you can use a dictionary to check the meaning. A dictionary gives you the **definition** of each word you look up.

**Example** **definition** *n.* stating the meaning of a word.

The words in a dictionary are listed in **alphabetical order** to make it easier for you to find them.

**Did you know?**

The most famous early dictionary was compiled by Samuel Johnson. It took him nearly nine years and was finally published in 1755.

## Activities

**1** Use a **dictionary** to check the meaning of the words in **bold**. Write what you **think** it means **before** looking in the dictionary and then add the dictionary **definition**.

| | Word | Before looking in the dictionary | Dictionary definition |
|---|---|---|---|
| a | It came to an **abrupt** stop. | | |
| b | She looked **dishevelled**. | | |
| c | Amir was **irritable** all day. | | |
| d | The land was **parched**. | | |
| e | The note was just **legible**. | | |
| f | She is not really **malicious**. | | |
| g | He has a **temporary** job. | | |
| h | I will not **tolerate** rudeness. | | |

**2** Use a dictionary to check the meaning of **three** words from the activity on page 4. Write the words and the dictionary definitions in the boxes below.

| Word | Dictionary definition |
|---|---|
| | |
| | |
| | |

# Word roots and word families

## Explanation

Another way of understanding what words mean is to learn about **root words**. Many words are formed from a root word with other bits added to the start or end. Words that share the same root word belong to the same **word family** and have **related meanings**. Recognising the root word often gives a clue to the meaning of a new word.

Example  act → **act**ion    **act**ive    **act**ivity    in**act**ive    re**act**    **act**or

All these words are formed from the root word 'act', so their meanings are also linked.

## Activities

**1**  Look closely at these words. Underline the **root word** that gives a **clue** to the meaning.

| | | |
|---|---|---|
| **a** redirection | **f** adjoining | **k** unusually |
| **b** repossession | **g** imprisonment | **l** enclosed |
| **c** misinformation | **h** quarrelsome | **m** deformed |
| **d** discoloured | **i** quizzical | **n** mountainous |
| **e** enabled | **j** infantile | **o** unrivalled |

**2**  Write a **root or family word** that helps you understand the related word in **bold**. Then write a **definition** of the related word.

| | Root or family word | Related word | Definition of related word |
|---|---|---|---|
| **a** | | a **fictitious** event | |
| **b** | | a **nondescript** place | |
| **c** | | a stolen **artefact** | |
| **d** | | **particles** of food | |
| **e** | | we want **equality** | |
| **f** | | a **typical** teenager | |

# Prefixes and meanings 1

## Explanation

Understanding how words are **formed** can help you understand word meanings. Many words are formed by taking a **root word** and adding groups of letters called **prefixes** to the beginning.

Example  open → reopen    (**Re–** means 'again' so 'reopen' means to open again.)

Prefixes **change the meaning** of root words so it is important to know what they mean.

Example  **pre–** before    **co–** joint, together    **mis–** badly, wrongly

## Activities

**1**  Use the **prefixes re–, pre–, co–** and **mis–** and these **root words** to form 15 words.
(You can use the root words and prefixes more than once.)

| view | write |
|------|-------|
| behave | fix |
| read | operate |
| place | exist |
| calculate | judge |

_____  _____  _____

_____  _____  _____

_____  _____  _____

_____  _____  _____

_____  _____  _____

Some prefixes change the meaning of the root word to make a word with the **opposite or negative meaning**.

Example  active (working or moving) → inactive (*not* working, or still)

These prefixes are important:  **in–    dis–    de–    un–    non–    im–    il–**

**2**  Add a prefix at the beginning of each word to make it mean the **opposite**.

a  _____ compose    f  _____ visible    k  _____ legal

b  _____ easy       g  _____ agree      l  _____ human

c  _____ polite     h  _____ sense      m  _____ obey

d  _____ code       i  _____ patient    n  _____ happy

e  _____ approve    j  _____ certain    o  _____ possible

Vocabulary

# Prefixes and meanings 2

## Explanation

Some words start with **prefixes** that may seem familiar. Looking at the start of words with the same prefix can help you think about their meanings.

Example **tele–** → **tele**scope    **tele**vision    **tele**photo    **tele**graph    **tele**phone

**tele–** means 'far off'. All these words refer to inventions that let us see or hear things that are far off.

## Activities

1  Here are some **prefixes** and their meanings. Use a **dictionary** to find **four** words that start with the same prefix. Make sure the word meanings are related to the meanings of the prefixes.

   **a  anti**  _____    _____    _____    _____
   (against)

   **b  auto**  _____    _____    _____    _____
   (self/own)

   **c  super**  _____    _____    _____    _____
   (more than/above/beyond)

   **d  inter**  _____    _____    _____    _____
   (between/among)

   **e  sub**  _____    _____    _____    _____
   (under)

2  Form **six** whole words from these prefixes and root words.

| mega | micro | mono |
|------|-------|------|
| wave | marine | rail |
| phone | ultra | aqua |
| sound | violet | |

_____    _____

_____    _____

_____    _____

## Did you know?

Some of these prefixes can be found in other languages as well.
**Example  auto**bahn ('motorway' in German)    **sub**marine ('underwater' in Spanish)
        **auto**route ('motorway' in French)    **sub**acqueo ('underwater' in Italian)

# Suffixes and word classes 1

## Explanation

Lots of words are formed by taking a **root word** and adding a group of letters called a **suffix** to the end. Adding suffixes creates **new words** that can be used in different ways.

Example **sweet** → sweet**er** (comparative)     sweet**ly** (adverb)

Adding a suffix changes the **type of word** but the meaning is still **related** to the root word.

## Activities

**1** Add the **suffix** that would make these words into **adverbs**.

a   silent _____         d   secure _____         g   urgent _____         j   willing _____

b   hesitant _____       e   jealous _____         h   usual _____          k   perfect _____

c   secret _____         f   brief _____           i   swift _____           l   excited _____

**2** Add suffixes to the words in **bold** so that these sentences makes sense.

a   I was **quick**_____ than Theo but Indira was **quick**_____ of all.

b   I am **tall**_____ than Jess but Stella is the **tall**_____ of us all.

Some **suffixes** change words into **adjectives** (or describing words).

Example **fool** → fool**ish**    **water** → water**y**    **fear** → fear**ful**    fear**less**    fear**some**

**3** Change these words into **adjectives** by adding a suffix from the box.

| –ful   –able   –less   –y   –some   –al   –ous |

a   comfort _____       f   cheer _____        k   quarrel _____

b   music _____         g   tear _____         l   peace _____

c   fashion _____       h   harm _____         m   worth _____

d   accident _____      i   child _____        n   sneak _____

e   poison _____        j   laugh _____         o   youth _____

# Suffixes and word classes 2

## Explanation

Adding a **suffix** to the end of a word often changes the type or **class of word**.

**Example sweet** → sweet**en** (verb)     sweet**ness** (noun)

Some suffixes form **verbs** and others form **nouns**. Verbs can describe actions or processes (to sweeten), while nouns can name things or qualities (sweetness).

## Activities

**1**  Use **suffixes** from the box to complete the **verbs** in these sentences.

| Verb suffixes |
|---|
| –ate |
| –ise |
| –ify |
| –en |

a  United equal_____.

b  Ice cubes solid_____.

c  Builders modern_____.

d  Doctors medic_____.

e  Shadows length_____.

f  Tight_____ our belts.

g  Class_____ these plants.

h  Blenders liquid_____.

i  Loud noises deaf_____.

j  Critics critic_____.

**2**  Change these words into **nouns** by selecting the correct suffix from the **noun generator** box. Write the nouns in the empty column. The first one has been done for you.

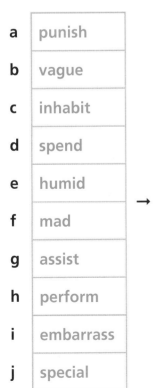

| | | Noun generator | |
|---|---|---|---|
| a | punish | | punishment |
| b | vague | | |
| c | inhabit | | |
| d | spend | –ness  –ity | |
| e | humid | –ment  –ant | |
| f | mad | –er  –ist | |
| g | assist | | |
| h | perform | | |
| i | embarrass | | |
| j | special | | |

# Homographs 1

## Explanation

**Homographs** are words that look the same because they have the **same spelling**, but they have **different meanings**.

**Example  bark**  **1** noise made by a dog
**2** the woody outer layer of a tree trunk

When you are reading, look at how these words are used. The rest of the sentence will help you to decide which meaning is correct.

## Activities

**1**  Tick the **correct** meaning of the **homograph** in each sentence.

**a**  We sat on the grassy **bank**. → slope ☐
→ place for keeping money ☐

**b**  The doctor **rose** to her feet. → flower ☐
→ got up ☐

**c**  Record the information in a **table**. → columns of facts ☐
→ piece of furniture ☐

**2**  Write **five** sentences to show **different** meanings of these words.

**a**  fan  meaning 1: _____

meaning 2: _____

**b**  train  meaning 1: _____

meaning 2: _____

meaning 3: _____

## Did you know?

Jokes are often based on homographs and their different meanings.
**Example**  Did you hear about the leopard that tried to escape? He was spotted!

# Homographs 2

Some homographs look the same but have **different pronunciations** as well as **different meanings**.

**Example** There was a **tear** in her jumper. (a rip)

Dad had to **tear** after him. (run, dash)

A **tear** ran down her cheek. (teardrop)

The rest of the sentence helps you to decide which **meaning** makes sense and which **pronunciation** is needed.

**Did you know?**

Homographs exist because the English language developed over a long period with different words being added at different times. A new version of the word would be added to an old one. No-one noticed a problem until centuries later, but by then it was too late.

| **Example** | **bark** | |
|---|---|---|
| **1** of a dog | Old English, came first |
| **2** of a tree | Old Norse, added later |

## Activities

**1** Find **one** word that can complete **both** sentences.

**a** I wrapped up the birthday _____ and tied the ribbon.

The mayor came to _____ me with my prize.

**b** She broke the _____ in her pencil.

Keep your dog on its _____ in the street.

**c** _____ the door.

Let's all keep _____ together.

**2** Write a sentence to show a different **meaning** and **pronunciation** of the word in **bold**.

**a** The actors took a **bow**. _____.

**b** Wait a **minute**. _____.

**c** Sit on the front **row**. _____.

**d** He **wound** up the clock. _____.

**e** I can speak **Polish**. _____.

# Collecting words

## Explanation

It is a good idea to **collect** interesting words that you meet when **reading** – particularly words that you could use in your **writing**. Write these words in a **notebook** in case you forget them. Make sure you understand what a word means before you try it out.

**Example ecstatic** (meaning 'thrilled')

So you could use this to describe the fans when their team scores a goal, the person who has just won the lottery, or your brother who was given tickets to see his favourite band.

## Activities

**1** Here are five interesting words. Write the **meaning** of each word, using a **dictionary** to help if needed.

**a** | morsel | _____

**b** | illuminated | _____

**c** | ramshackle | _____

**d** | dismal | _____

**e** | exquisite | _____

**2** Now decide which word above **best fits** in each of these sentences. Write the word in the space.

**a** The house was a _____ , run-down sort of place.

**b** There was not a _____ of food left in the house.

**c** The carvings on the box were _____ .

**d** It was a _____ day. It never stopped raining.

**e** The trees were _____ by the soft moonlight.

### Did you know?

You have two lots of words in your word memory – the words that you understand and the words that you use. You probably know and understand a lot more words than you usually use.

# Word showers

## Explanation

Before you start writing about a subject, write down lots of **possible words** you could use. Write the **subject** in the middle of a piece of paper. Then think of all the words you could use and write them round the outside, as a **word shower**. Choose interesting words, less obvious choices and words you have collected from reading.

## Activities

1   Complete this **word shower**. See how many words you can think of to describe the sea. A few boxes have been done for you.

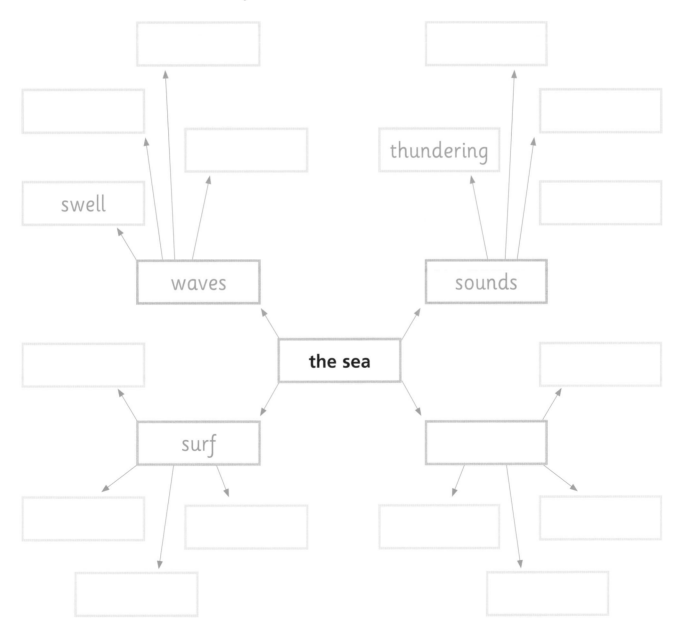

# Choosing words 1

## Explanation

When you are writing, **don't use the first word** that comes into your head. Stop and think again. Think about other words you know. **Try out a number of words** in your sentence before making your final choice. Choose the word that works best.

**Example** The man **walked** down the street.

If you think again, you will come up with better, more effective words than 'walked'.

**Example  walked** → strolled     marched     strode     plodded

## Activities

**1**  Here are some sentences that use ordinary, everyday words. Try some other words to **replace** the word that has been crossed out. **Choose a better word** and write it in.

**a**   There was a(n) ~~big~~ _____ pile of rubbish by the door.

**b**   I enjoyed the book. It was very ~~good~~ _____ .

**c**   We talked to the old lady for a while. She seemed very ~~nice~~ _____ .

**d**   I ~~got~~ _____ a prize for winning the competition.

**e**   I was ~~scared~~ _____ by the sudden noise.

**f**   The boy looked very ~~sad~~ _____ .

**2**  The word '**said**' is used a lot. Here are some words you might use instead. Choose the **best word** to use in each sentence.

| yelled | asked | pleaded | laughed | whispered |
| --- | --- | --- | --- | --- |

**a**   'Shh, or they will hear you,' _____ Lee.

**b**   'Where do you live?' _____ Abdul.

**c**   'Help! Let me out of here!' _____ Charlotte.

**d**   'You must be joking!' _____ Sheenia.

**e**   'It's my turn. Let me try,' _____ Ravi.

# Choosing words 2

## Explanation

When choosing words, always be as **precise** as possible. If you are writing about a shop, the word 'shop' is rather vague. Choose a word that describes exactly or names the **particular type** of shop.

**Example  shop** → supermarket      department store      bakery                    sweetshop
                          butcher                   delicatessen            health-food shop       bookshop
                          newsagent              shoe shop                 toyshop                   florist

Words like these create a much **clearer picture** for the reader.

## Activities

**1**    Write **four** words that could be used in place of these **nouns** to give a **clearer** picture.

| a | book | | c | flower | | e | house |
|---|------|---|---|--------|---|---|-------|
| | dictionary | | | rose | | | bungalow |
| | | | | | | | |
| | | | | | | | |
| | | | | | | | |

| b | hat | | d | shoes | | f | boat |
|---|-----|---|---|-------|---|---|------|
| | sombrero | | | sandals | | | kayak |
| | | | | | | | |
| | | | | | | | |
| | | | | | | | |

**2**    **Improve** these sentences by changing the words in **bold** to **more precise** ones.
Choose words that create clear pictures.

**a**   A **bird** _____ sang in the **tree** _____ .

**b**   I put the **book** _____ in my **bag** _____ .

**c**   We planted **flowers** _____ outside the **house** _____ .

**d**   A **car** _____ pulled up outside the **shop** _____ .

**e**   He wore **shoes** _____ and a **hat** _____ .

# Using a thesaurus 1

## Explanation

A **thesaurus** is a book that gives you a choice of **synonyms**, or words with **similar meanings**. Every writer should have a thesaurus. It can help you find just the word you need.

**Example** a **flash** of light

If you look up the word 'flash' in a thesaurus you will find a long list of words to choose from.

**Example** → beam ray spark blaze glare gleam
glint flicker twinkle sparkle glitter shimmer

## Activities

**1** Use a **thesaurus** to find at least **four** words with the **same or similar** meanings to these words.

| | Word | Meanings |
|---|---|---|
| **a** | beautiful | |
| **b** | happy | |
| **c** | bright | |
| **d** | look | |
| **e** | throw | |

## Did you know?

Peter Mark Roget wrote the first modern **thesaurus** in 1852. The word 'thesaurus' comes from an Ancient Greek word meaning 'a treasure store', and that's what a thesaurus is – a store of useful and interesting words.

# Synonyms

## Activities

**1** Match up pairs of words that have the **same** or **similar** meanings.

| amusing | adore |
|---------|-------|
| angry | penniless |
| strong | intelligent |
| stop | humorous |
| clever | assist |
| like | prevent |
| poor | powerful |
| help | annoyed |

_____ and _____

_____ and _____

_____ and _____

_____ and _____

_____ and _____

_____ and _____

_____ and _____

_____ and _____

**2** It is **useful to know** synonyms for words you use a lot. Write a **synonym** for each of these words.

**a** great _____

**b** horrible _____

**c** rich _____

**d** shout _____

**e** little _____

**f** stupid _____

**g** quiet _____

**h** run _____

# Using a thesaurus 2

## Explanation

Not all synonyms given in a thesaurus mean *exactly* the same as the word you looked up. Some have only **similar meanings**. When you are writing, you must decide which word **best fits** the situation and describes what you are trying to say.

**Example** Was the **flash** of light:

a **beam** of light?  a **shimmer** of light?  a **blaze** of light?  a **flicker** of light?

All these words have slightly different meanings and create different pictures and effects.

## Activities

**1** Here are some **synonyms** for the word 'sad'. Choose the **best word** to use in each sentence.

> unhappy    tearful    miserable    downhearted

a  The little boy sobbed and looked at me with a _____ face.

b  Ashia had a cold and was feeling _____.

c  When we let in the fifth goal we were quite _____.

d  We were _____ about the decision but could do nothing.

**2** Use a different synonym to replace the word '**runs**' in each of these sentences. Choose a synonym that **best fits** each sentence. Use a **thesaurus** to help.

a  Dad **runs** _____ to keep fit.

b  The crab **runs** _____ under a rock.

c  The athlete **runs** _____ to the line.

d  The man **runs** _____ in from the rain.

e  The squirrel **runs** _____ across the grass.

f  She suddenly **runs** _____ for the door.

Vocabulary

# Antonyms

## Explanation

**Antonyms** are words with completely **opposite** meanings. If you look in a **thesaurus**, you may find the opposites of words are also given.

**Example young** → old    **hot** → cold    **start** → stop    **happy** → unhappy

Some words have more than one antonym.

**Example silly** → sensible, clever

## Activities

**1**  Match up the pairs of opposites or **antonyms**. Write the pairs of words on the right.

| | |
|---|---|
| easy | negative |
| ancient | rough |
| smooth | cowardly |
| close | difficult |
| positive | distant |
| huge | modern |
| cheerful | tiny |
| heroic | glum |

_____ and _____

_____ and _____

_____ and _____

_____ and _____

_____ and _____

_____ and _____

_____ and _____

_____ and _____

**2**  Complete these sentences using pairs of antonyms.

**a**  Cinderella's sisters were _____ but the Fairy Godmother was _____ .

**b**  The Giant was _____ but Jack was _____ .

**c**  The hare was _____ but the tortoise was _____ .

**d**  Peter Pan was _____ but Captain Hook was _____ .

**e**  Robin Hood was _____ but the Sheriff of Nottingham was _____ .

# Shades of meaning 1

Words that you find listed in a **thesaurus** often have **different shades of meaning**.

**Example angry** → irritated   annoyed   displeased,   cross   livid   enraged   furious,

suggest a **mild** anger ──────→ suggest much **stronger** feelings

It is important to recognise different shades of meaning in similar words.

## Activities

**1**   Sort these words into **two sets** to show different **shades** of meaning.

**a**   It was a **hot** day.

| warm   scorching   boiling   sweltering   mild   fine |
|---|

| Fairly hot | Very hot |
|---|---|
|  |  |
|  |  |
|  |  |

**b**   I was **happy** to be there.

| glad   delighted   thrilled   pleased   joyful   ecstatic   content |
|---|

| Fairly happy | Very happy |
|---|---|
|  |  |
|  |  |
|  |  |
|  |  |

**2**   Use a thesaurus to help you add words showing different shades of meaning.

**a**   (a little wet)   _____   →   _____   (very wet)

**b**   (a little thin)   _____   →   _____   (very thin)

**c**   (quite good)   _____   →   _____   (very good)

**d**   (a little strange) _____   →   _____   (very strange)

Vocabulary

# Shades of meaning 2

## Explanation

Words with **similar meanings** can create very **different effects**. You can compare these effects in different sentences.

**Example**  He **grabbed** the money.        He **clutched** the money.

The words 'grabbed' and 'clutched' have similar meanings, but the effect is quite different. The person who grabbed the money might be a thief. The one who clutched the money sounds more like someone who is scared or desperate.

## Activities

**1**  A writer decided to use the following **verbs** (in **bold**). Why did they choose each word?

a  I **admire** her music.        _____

b  I **demand** an answer.        _____

c  He **tossed** it away.        _____

d  Water **seeped** under the door.        _____

e  She **glowered** at him.        _____

f  He moved **softly**.        _____

g  They **hesitated** at the gate.        _____

**2**  Underline the word that **best** creates the **effect** shown.

| | Effect |
|---|---|
| a  He cast   lobbed   hurled it away. | → shows he is angry |
| b  She tugged   hauled   pulled it up. | → shows it is heavy |
| c  We know  believe   suppose it is true. | → shows we are certain |
| d  He munched   devoured   consumed every crumb. | → shows he is very hungry |
| e  I found a shadowy   shady   murky corner. | → sounds pleasant |
| f  They creep   sneak   inch away. | → shows they move very, very slowly |

# Choosing words for effect

## Activities

**1** **Replace** the word that has been crossed out with a **stronger** word. Use a **thesaurus** to help.

a Mum was ~~cross~~ _____ .

b You have ~~damaged~~ _____ my car.

c I ~~dislike~~ _____ salt and vinegar flavour.

d It was ~~very~~ _____ dangerous.

e It was a ~~good~~ _____ performance.

f There was a ~~fine~~ _____ view.

**2** Here are some **synonyms** for the word '**walked**'. Choose the word that most effectively shows the **feelings** of the character in each sentence.

| paced | trudged | marched | strolled | stepped | wandered |
|-------|---------|---------|----------|---------|----------|

a He sadly _____ down the road.

b She _____ happily along.

c We nervously _____ the room.

d Angrily, she _____ down the corridor.

e They aimlessly _____ the streets.

f Carefully, they _____ onto the platform.

**3** Write **two sentences** to describe a **thunderstorm**. Choose words that make it sound **threatening**.

_____

_____

# Practising synonyms and antonyms

**1** Underline the word **closest in meaning** to the word in **bold**.

a It's an **absurd** idea.      good      interesting      ridiculous      clever

b He was **elated** by the news.      angry      overjoyed      frightened      tired

c We must **persevere**.      return      overtake      stop      continue

**2** Write a **synonym** for the word in bold.

a the **victorious** team _____      c an **abundant** supply _____

b a **hilarious** story _____      d an **ordinary** day _____

**3** Underline the **two** words that mean the **opposite** of the word in bold.

a The place was **deserted**.      empty      busy      abandoned      crowded

b The family were **poor**.      wealthy      needy      prosperous      healthy

c The aliens were **hostile**.      surprised      welcoming      approachable      aggressive

**4** Write an **antonym** of each word.

a shallow _____      d probable _____

b absent _____      e partial _____

c broad _____      f demolish _____

**5** Choose the **most suitable** synonym for 'old' to use in each phrase.

| ancient | prehistoric | elderly | outdated | antique | previous |
|---|---|---|---|---|---|

a _____ vase      c _____ monument      e _____ cave

b _____ man      d _____ clothes      f my _____ school

**6** Put a **prefix** at the beginning of each word to make it into an antonym.

a _____ understand      d _____ important

b _____ capable      e _____ orderly

c _____ perfect      f _____ legible

# Formal and informal words 1

## Explanation

When looking for the right word, think about the people **who will read** your writing. Words you use when talking to people **you know well** might sound **out of place** when you are writing to someone you do not know or **want to impress**.

**Example** Lots of love     See you!  →  Yours sincerely     Yours faithfully

You could use the first two when **writing to a friend**, but only the last two would be suitable for a more **formal letter**.

## Activities

**1**  Here are some different ways of saying the same thing. Decide which you would use if writing **to a friend** and which you would use **to impress**. Complete the labels.

a   The special offer was **a rip-off**.  ⟶  to a friend

The special offer was **misleading**.  ⟶  to impress

b   They **blew** the money.  ⟶

They **squandered** the money.  ⟶

c   His haircut was **very fashionable**.  ⟶

His haircut was **really cool**.  ⟶

d   Jon felt **woozy**.  ⟶

Jon felt **light-headed**.  ⟶

e   I feel quite **dehydrated**.  ⟶

I am **dying for a drink**.  ⟶

f   He was a rather **dubious** character.  ⟶

He was a rather **dodgy** character.  ⟶

# Formal and informal words 2

## Explanation

If you are writing something **formal**, use formal words. Think about what sort of words the person you are writing to might use and use similar language yourself. You can look words up in a **thesaurus** to help you find a more formal version. There will often be several words to choose from.

**Example cheeky** → rude    impolite    disrespectful    forward

## Activities

**1**  Use a **thesaurus** to help you find **four** words that are more **formal** to use in place of these words.

| | | |
|---|---|---|
| **a** | cheap | inexpensive    reasonable    economical    affordable |
| **b** | give | |
| **c** | silly | |
| **d** | ugly | |
| **e** | scary | |
| **f** | tell | |
| **g** | easy | |
| **h** | test | |
| **i** | ask | |
| **j** | find | |

## Did you know?

Lots of formal words we use today came originally from French – words like 'accuse', 'pardon', 'request', 'enter', 'cease', 'require'. This dates back to the time after the Norman Conquest in 1066, when the most powerful people in the country spoke French.

# Old words

## Explanation

The English language is **always changing**. New words are **added** and other words **fall out of use** over time. Some words become old-fashioned, so people use them less often and eventually stop using them at all.

**Example**  sooth    anon    hath    thou

It is still important to know about old words like these because you might find them in books written a long time ago.

## Activities

**1**  Sort these words into **old words** that are not used much today and **newer words** that are used often.

| neckerchief    farthing<br><br>Velcro®    superstar<br><br>quoth    flagon<br><br>trainers    computer<br><br>video    parlour<br><br>clarion    rocket | **Old words** | **Newer words** |
|---|---|---|
| | | |

**2**  Some words die out because the item they describe is no longer used or has been replaced by a newer invention. Write some examples of words you might find in **history books** but do not use every day, related to the topic areas below.

**a  writing** _quill_

**b  transport** _carriage_

**c  entertainment** _gramophone_

**d  household** _bellows_

# New meopings

## Explanation

Some words stay in use but their meaning changes over time.

**Example pretty** (**originally** 'tricky' or 'deceitful' **now** 'attractive')

Other words take on a new meaning and keep the original meaning too.

**Example** a **cool** breeze (**originally** 'coldish')

a **cool** band (**now** 'fashionable')

## Activities

**1** Write the **newer meaning** for each of these words.

Original meaning: woven threads or spider's cobweb

**a web**

Newer meaning: _____

Original meaning: small rodent

**b mouse**

Newer meaning: _____

Original meaning: sweet biscuit

**c cookies**

Newer meaning: _____

Original meaning: (noun) written or printed words

**d text**

Newer (verb) meaning: _____

Original meaning: (noun) small river

**e stream**

Newer (verb) meaning: _____

### Did you know?

The word 'terrific' originally meant 'causing terror'. Now we use it to mean 'great' or 'wonderful'.

# Forming new nouns 1

## Explanation

**New words** are always being **added** to the English language. New ideas or new inventions need new words to describe them. Many new words are made up of words or bits of words that already existed.

**Example** internet    hyperlink    webcam    download

## Activities

1   Look closely at these words. Write the **two** words that have been **blended** together to form a **new word**. Use a dictionary to help.

    **a**   emoticon   = _____ + _____

    **b**   heliport    = _____ + _____

    **c**   smog       = _____ + _____

    **d**   brunch     = _____ + _____

    **e**   motel       = _____ + _____

2   **Compound words** are made up of **two** or more existing **root words**. These compound words are muddled up. Sort them out to make **10 computing** terms. Write them in the box.

| keymark | spreadsaver | bookwall | netboard | homesheet |
|---|---|---|---|---|
| screenbase | lapup | firepage | backwork | datatop |

_____  _____  _____  _____  _____

_____  _____  _____  _____  _____

3   Add these **prefixes** to the **root words** to form words that have entered the English language in recent years.

| cyber | hyper | multi | mega |
|---|---|---|---|

    **a** _____ media       **e** _____ market       **i** _____ store

    **b** _____ text         **f** _____ star         **j** _____ link

    **c** _____ space       **g** _____ task         **k** _____ man

    **d** _____ byte        **h** _____ café        **l** _____ million

# Forming new nouns 2

People sometimes **invent** new words based on words that already exist.

**Example** maga**zine** (**originally** a thin book with lots of different articles)

fan**zine** (**now** a magazine written by fans of a particular celebrity genre or sports team)

## Activities

**1** Use the clues to help you complete the missing word.

**a** someone who can't stop **working**          workaholic

**b** someone who can't stop **shopping**          _____

**c** someone who can't stop **eating chocolate**          _____

**2** Write **three** words that have the **same ending** as each of these words.

**a** broad**cast**          _____ cast          _____ cast          _____ cast

**b** mar**athon**          _____ athon          _____ athon          _____ athon

**c** hard**ware**          _____ ware          _____ ware          _____ ware

Some words are formed by **shortening** a word that already exists.

**Example** photograph → **photo**          television → **telly**, TV

**3** Complete these tables so that they show the **original** word and the **shortened** word that came from it.

| | Original word | Shortened word |
|---|---|---|
| **a** | omnibus | |
| **b** | fanatic | |
| **c** | stereophonic | |
| **d** | quadrangle | |
| **e** | limousine | |

| | Original word | Shortened word |
|---|---|---|
| **f** | | demo |
| **g** | | fridge |
| **h** | | email |
| **i** | | app |
| **j** | | ad |

# The origin of words 1

## Explanation

Over time the English language has **borrowed** lots of words from **other languages**. In subjects such as science and maths you will find many words that originally came from **Latin** or **Greek**.

Example  science          (**origin** a Latin word meaning 'to know')

mathematics    (**origin** a Greek word meaning 'to learn')

## Activities

**1** Draw a line to match each word with its **meaning** and Latin or Greek **origin**.

sphere                    tenth (from Latin)

opaque                   less (from Latin)

equal                    ball (from Greek)

decimal                  greatest (from Latin)

maximum                  even/level (from Latin)

symbol                   alongside one another (from Greek)

minus                    shady/dark (from Latin)

parallel                 mark/token (from Greek)

**2** Write **two** words we use today that come from these **roots**. Use a dictionary to help.

| | Root word | Language | Words we use today |
|---|---|---|---|
| a | circus (a ring) | Latin | |
| b | skeletos (dried up) | Greek | |
| c | mobilis (moveable) | Latin | |
| d | phobos (fear) | Greek | |
| e | digitus (a finger) | Latin | |
| f | vacuus (empty) | Latin | |

## Did you know?

'Acrobat' and 'acrophobia' (fear of heights) come from the Greek 'akros' meaning 'topmost'.

# The origin of words 2

## Explanation

English has borrowed words from many different languages. This explains many of our unusual spellings.

**Example**  banana      guitar      tobacco      (Spanish)

shampoo      cheetah      bangle      (Hindi)

## Activities

**1**  Look closely at these geography terms. Underline the words that come from **another language**. Both the **spelling** and the **meaning** will give you a clue.

| | | | |
|---|---|---|---|
| hill | safari | cliff | avalanche |
| ski | town | volcano | field |
| house | chalet | typhoon | wood |
| wind | tsunami | flood | pagoda |

**2**  Write next to each word the language that you think these food words came from.

**a**  pasta  _____

**b**  naan  _____

**c**  sushi  _____

**d**  croissant  _____

**e**  chilli  _____

**f**  tortilla  _____

**g**  tandoori  _____

**h**  spaghetti  _____

**i**  satsuma  _____

**j**  meringue  _____

Urdu

Spanish

Japanese

Italian

French

## Did you know?

English has always borrowed words from other languages. As explorers travelled to different countries, words were added from all over the world.

**Example**  chocolate (Central America)      tea (China)      kangaroo (Australia)
pyjamas (India)      coffee (Turkey)

# Idioms

## Explanation

The English language is full of **idioms**. These are phrases that should **not be taken literally** because they do not mean exactly what they say.

**Example** 'Ah, yes. Jo Brown. That name **rings a bell**.'

It doesn't actually mean that the name makes a bell ring – just that it reminds you of something.

## Activities

**1**  **a**  Tick which **idiom** is represented by this cartoon.

    thrilled to bits ☐

    too big for his boots ☐

    break your word ☐

    under the weather ☐

  **b**  Explain what it means. _____

**2**  Explain the **meaning** of these idioms.

  **a**  to turn over a new leaf  _____

  **b**  a piece of cake  _____

  **c**  all in the same boat  _____

  **d**  over the moon  _____

  **e**  easier said than done  _____

  **f**  to hold your tongue  _____

  **g**  to have a lot on your plate  _____

  **h**  to be found wanting  _____

  **i**  to pull a fast one  _____

## Did you know?

The phrase 'to put a sock in it' means 'to be quiet'. It may originate from the time when gramophone (record) players had no volume control. To make it quieter, you put a sock inside the trumpet, where the sound came out.

Vocabulary

# Idioms and similes

## Explanation

To understand **figurative** language such as **similes**, you have to go beyond the actual words and think about the **effect**.

**Example**  to run like the wind.

On one level, this simile doesn't make sense – the wind cannot run. To understand the meaning you have to think about your experiences of a windy day and the feeling of the wind rushing past.

## Activities

**1**  Draw lines to match these well-known **similes** with their **meanings**.

as cool as a cucumber                sure to get an angry reaction

as bright as a button                very quick and sudden

like a red rag to a bull             very calm, untroubled

moved like lightning                 intelligent, alert, lively

**2**  What is the writer trying to tell us in the following similes?

**a**  wires like a plate of spaghetti

_____

**b**  a smile like a shark

_____

**c**  a mind like a sponge

_____

**d**  icing like mountain peaks

_____

### Did you know?

We use the phrase 'as good as gold' to mean 'well behaved' but how can gold be well behaved? Originally, 'good' in this phrase referred to the gold being genuine, not fake or forged like bank notes might be. But over time, the phrase just came to mean 'good' behaviour.

# Onomatopoeia

## Explanation

**Onomatopoeia** refers to words that **sound like the noise** they are describing.

**Example** crash    pop    bleep    hum

It is easy to see, or hear, how these words were invented. Someone simply **made up a word** that sounds like the noise.

## Activities

**1** Sort these **onomatopoeic words** into **three** groups according to the sort of sound they describe.

| | | | | |
|---|---|---|---|---|
| slosh | bong | hum | splash | clatter |
| splish | crash | pitter-patter | squeak | slop |
| swish | plop | boom | thud | swoosh |

| Watery sounds | Soft/quiet sounds | Loud sounds |
|---|---|---|
| | | |
| | | |
| | | |
| | | |
| | | |

**2** Think of some **onomatopoeic words** to describe each of these sound pictures.

**a** someone falling into a duck pond

_____

**b** opening a cupboard so that everything falls out

_____

**c** a car skidding and crashing into a lamppost

_____

# Using your vocabulary

**1**  Rewrite these sentences using more **formal** vocabulary.

a  We have loads of ideas to chew over.

_____

b  Please fill in the form when you get it and send it back quickly.

_____

c  It was bad luck that the car whacked a lamppost and smashed into the lorry.

_____

**2**  Underline the word that **best** completes each sentence.

a  Amy **slumped**  **collapsed**  **sprawled** contentedly on the sofa.

b  I love the **gaudy**  **vibrant**  **garish** colours.

c  The flood waters **streamed**  **flowed**  **surged** through the streets.

d  We **trampled**  **squelched**  **plodded** through the slush.

e  In a panic, he **flew**  **ambled**  **jogged** down the stairs.

**3**  **Edit** this extract from a story. Try making it sound **more interesting** by improving the **choice of words**. Choose words to give a sense of **danger and excitement**.

Casper ran forward and took the burning torch from the wall.

The dragon turned round and looked at him. Scared, Casper madly

waved the torch at  the angry dragon. The dragon put up its head and

roared a big roar. Smoke came out of its nose and flames came out

of its big mouth. The hot breath made Casper go back fast.

# Now you try

## Treasury of words

Start collecting interesting words. Write them in a special notebook or on bits of paper that you can keep in a special box. Collect words that you think you might find useful, and use a dictionary to find out what they mean.

## Word of the day

Choose a word that you don't usually use and try to use it at least once during the day, either when speaking or writing. Make sure you have a good understanding of the word's meaning to help you use it at the right time and in the right way.

## Power read

Read something that you don't usually read, such as the news pages in the newspaper, part of a gardening book or a cookery magazine. This is a good way of finding new words that you have not met before. See if you can work out the meaning of these words. Use a dictionary to help.

## Word game challenge

Challenge your friends to a word game. Try 'Synonym race' – see who can think of the most synonyms for a word in a minute. Or 'Call my bluff' – choose an unusual word from the dictionary and write down the definition. Make up two false definitions as well, and ask your friends to pick out the true one.

## Make a glossary

Keep a list of new words you meet in subjects such as maths, geography or science. When you have 10 words, put them in alphabetical order. Make sure you understand what each word means and write definitions. Add an example or a picture if it helps.

## Word collage

Choose a set of synonyms (for example, 'quick', 'swift', 'rapid', 'high-speed', 'brisk') and related antonyms (for example, 'slow', 'unhurried', 'dawdling'). Collect pictures to illustrate the contrasts and shades of meaning in the words. Make a collage to display the words and pictures together.

# Answers

## Page 4: Understanding word meanings 1

**1**

| | Word | Meaning |
|---|---|---|
| a | frail | weak or fragile |
| b | vain | proud or conceited about one's appearance |
| c | billow | move in large waves |
| d | plunge | dive or fall suddenly |
| e | weary | tired |
| f | commence | begin or start |
| g | location | place |
| h | isolated | alone, lonely or cut off |
| i | adequate | just enough |

## Page 5: Understanding word meanings 2

**1**
- **a** strong
- **b** tasty
- **c** knocked out of
- **d** go round
- **e** stop
- **f** copy
- **g** dangerous

## Page 6: Using a dictionary

**1**

| | Word | Dictionary definition |
|---|---|---|
| a | abrupt | sudden or hasty |
| b | dishevelled | ruffled and untidy |
| c | irritable | easily annoyed |
| d | parched | very dry |
| e | legible | clear enough to read |
| f | malicious | spiteful |
| g | temporary | lasting for a limited time only |
| h | tolerate | allow or put up with something unpleasant |

**2** You might have chosen any three words and found dictionary definitions for them.

## Page 7: Word roots and word families

**1**
- **a** re**direct**ion
- **b** re**possess**ion
- **c** mis**inform**ation
- **d** dis**colour**ed
- **e** en**able**d
- **f** ad**join**ing
- **g** im**prison**ment
- **h** **quarrel**some
- **i** **quiz**zical
- **j** **infant**ile
- **k** un**usual**ly
- **l** en**close**d
- **m** de**form**ed
- **n** **mountain**ous
- **o** un**rival**led

| | Root or family word | Related word | Definition of related word |
|---|---|---|---|
| a | fiction, fictional | a **fictitious** event | imagined, made up, did not really happen |
| b | description, descriptive, describe | a **nondescript** place | having no special features to describe |
| c | art, artist | a stolen **artefact** | a made object, a piece of art or craftwork |
| d | part | **particles** of food | tiny amounts, very small pieces |
| e | equal | we want **equality** | being equal |
| f | type | a **typical** teenager | the usual kind or sort |

## Page 8: Prefixes and meanings 1

**1** Any 15 of these words.

| | | | | |
|---|---|---|---|---|
| **re**view | **re**read | **re**write | **re**place | **re**calculate |
| **pre**view | **pre**judge | **pre**fix | **pre**-exist | |
| **co**-operate | **co**-exist | **co**-write | | |
| **mis**read | **mis**judge | **mis**place | **mis**behave | **mis**calculate |

**2**
- **a** **de**compose
- **b** **un**easy
- **c** **im**polite
- **d** **de**code
- **e** **dis**approve
- **f** **in**visible
- **g** **dis**agree
- **h** **non**sense
- **i** **im**patient
- **j** **un**certain
- **k** **il**legal
- **l** **in**human
- **m** **dis**obey
- **n** **un**happy
- **o** **im**possible

## Page 9: Prefixes and meanings 2

**1** These are some of the words you might have found.
- **a anti** antibiotic, antifreeze, antibody, antiseptic, antidote, antivirus
- **b auto** automatic, automate, automobile, autopilot, autobiography, autograph
- **c super** supermarket, superstar, superstructure, supernatural, supersonic
- **d inter** international, interval, intermission, interplanetary, interlude, interface
- **e sub** subterranean, submarine, subway, submerge, subordinate

**2** Any six of these words.

| | | | |
|---|---|---|---|
| megaphone | microphone | microwave | aquamarine |
| ultramarine | ultraviolet | ultrasound | monorail |

## Page 10: Suffixes and word classes 1

**1**
- **a** silent**ly**
- **b** hesitant**ly**
- **c** secret**ly**
- **d** secure**ly**
- **e** jealous**ly**
- **f** brief**ly**
- **g** urgent**ly**
- **h** usual**ly**
- **i** swift**ly**
- **j** willing**ly**
- **k** perfect**ly**
- **l** excited**ly**

**2**
- **a** I was quick**er** than Theo but Indira was quick**est** of all.
- **b** I am tall**er** than Jess but Stella is the tall**est** of us all.

**3**
- **a** comfort**able**/comfort**less**
- **b** music**al**
- **c** fashion**able**
- **d** accident**al**
- **e** poison**ous**
- **f** cheer**ful**/cheer**y**/cheer**less**
- **g** tear**ful**/tear**y**/tear**less**
- **h** harm**ful**/harm**less**
- **i** child**less**
- **j** laugh**able**
- **k** quarrel**some**
- **l** peace**ful**/peace**able**
- **m** worth**less**/worth**y**
- **n** sneak**y**
- **o** youth**ful**

## Page 11: Suffixes and word classes 2

**1**
- **a** United equal**ise**.
- **b** Ice cubes solid**ify**.
- **c** Builders modern**ise**.
- **d** Doctors medic**ate**.
- **e** Shadows length**en**.
- **f** Tight**en** our belts.
- **g** Class**ify** these plants.
- **h** Blenders liquid**ise**.
- **i** Loud noises deaf**en**.
- **j** Critics critic**ise**.

**2**  **a** punishment

**b** vague**ness**

**c** inhabit**ant**

**d** spend**er**

**e** humid**ity**

**f** mad**ness**

**g** assist**ant**

**h** perform**er**

**i** embarrass**ment**

**j** special**ist**/special**ity**

## Page 12: Homographs 1

**1**  **a** slope        **b** got up        **c** columns of facts

**2**  These are just examples of sentences to show the different meanings

**a fan**

1  I put the fan on to keep cool.

2  He is a United fan.

**b train**

1  A train runs on rails.

2  The Queen's dress had a long train.

3  I train at the track every Wednesday.

## Page 13: Homographs 2

**1**  **a** present        **b** lead        **c** close

**2**  These are just examples of sentences to show the different meanings.

**a** Robin Hood had a **bow** and arrow.

**b** Specks of dust are **minute**.

**c** They had a terrible **row**.

**d** He had a head **wound**.

**e** **Polish** the floor.

## Page 14: Collecting words

**1**  **a morsel**        a scrap or a very small piece

**b illuminated**    lit up

**c ramshackle**    rickety and tumbledown

**d dismal**        gloomy and dull

**e exquisite**    very fine or delicate

**2**  **a** The house was a **ramshackle**, run-down sort of place.

**b** There was not a **morsel** of food left in the house.

**c** The carvings on the box were **exquisite**.

**d** It was a **dismal** day. It never stopped raining.

**e** The trees were **illuminated** by the soft moonlight.

## Page 15: Word showers

**1** Here are just a few suggestions. You might have thought of other words.

**waves**   swell, ripples, breakers, wash, surging, smashing

**sounds**   thundering, roar, boom, whoosh, rumble, whisper, swish

**surf**     foaming, froth, snowy, bubbles, spray, mist

**mood words/appearance**   shimmer, angry, soothing, turquoise, glimmer

## Page 16: Choosing words 1

**1** These are just suggestions; you might have thought of some other interesting words to use.

a  There was an **enormous** pile of rubbish by the door.

b  I enjoyed the book. It was very **interesting**.

c  We talked to the old lady for a while. She seemed very **friendly**.

d  I **received** a prize for winning the competition.

e  I was **startled** by the sudden noise.

f  The boy looked very **tearful**.

**2**  a  'Shh, or they will hear you,' **whispered** Lee.

b  'Where do you live?' **asked** Abdul.

c  'Help! Let me out of here!' **yelled** Charlotte.

d  'You must be joking!' **laughed** Sheenia.

e  'It's my turn. Let me try,' **pleaded** Ravi.

## Page 17: Choosing words 2

**1** These are just a few of the words you might have included in your lists.

| a | book | c | flower | e | house |
|---|---|---|---|---|---|
| | dictionary | | rose | | bungalow |
| | encyclopaedia | | tulip | | flat |
| | atlas | | daffodil | | mansion |
| | textbook | | primrose | | cottage |

| b | hat | d | shoes | f | boat |
|---|---|---|---|---|---|
| | sombrero | | sandals | | kayak |
| | baseball cap | | flip-flops | | barge |
| | beanie | | slippers | | ferry |
| | flat cap | | trainers | | yacht |

**2** These are just a few possibilities. There are lots of words you could have chosen to create different pictures.

a  A **nightingale** sang in the **oak tree**.

b  I put the **photo album** in my **rucksack**.

c  We planted **sunflowers** outside the **cottage**.

d  A **taxi** pulled up outside the **department store**.

e  He wore **trainers** and a **baseball cap**.

## Page 18: Using a thesaurus 1

**1** These are just a few of the words you might have found in the thesaurus.

|   | Words | Meanings |
|---|---|---|
| a | beautiful | attractive, lovely, gorgeous, stunning |
| b | happy | joyful, merry, pleased, delighted, content |
| c | bright | gleaming, glistening, glowing, brilliant, dazzling |
| d | look | glance, peek, gaze, stare, peep |
| e | throw | hurl, sling, toss, fling, bowl, lob |

## Page 19: Synonyms

**1**

| amusing | humorous | clever | intelligent |
|---|---|---|---|
| angry | annoyed | like | adore |
| strong | powerful | poor | penniless |
| stop | prevent | help | assist |

**2** These are just suggestions, as these words have many synonyms.

a **great** wonderful  
b **horrible** awful  
c **rich** wealthy  
d **shout** yell  

e **little** tiny  
f **stupid** foolish  
g **quiet** peaceful  
h **run** sprint  

## Page 20: Using a thesaurus 2

**1**
a The little boy sobbed and looked at me with a **tearful** face.
b Ashia had a cold and was feeling **miserable**.
c When we let in the fifth goal we were quite **downhearted**.
d We were **unhappy** about the decision but could do nothing.

**2** Other choices are possible.
a Dad **jogs** to keep fit.
b The crab **scuttles** under a rock.
c The athlete **sprints** to the line.
d The man **hurries** in from the rain.
e The squirrel **scampers** across the grass.
f She suddenly **darts** for the door.

## Page 21: Antonyms

**1**

| easy | difficult | positive | negative |
|---|---|---|---|
| ancient | modern | huge | tiny |
| smooth | rough | cheerful | glum |
| close | distant | heroic | cowardly |

**2** These are just suggestions. Other pairs of antonyms could be used.

a Cinderella's sisters were **cruel** but the Fairy Godmother was **kind**.

b The Giant was **rich** but Jack was **penniless**.

c The hare was **foolish/fast** but the tortoise was **clever/slow**.

d Peter Pan was **good** but Captain Hook was **evil**.

e Robin Hood was **generous** but the Sheriff of Nottingham was **selfish**.

## Page 22: Shades of meaning 1

**1** a

| Fairly hot | Very hot |
|---|---|
| warm | scorching |
| mild | boiling |
| fine | sweltering |

b

| Fairly happy | Very happy |
|---|---|
| glad | delighted |
| pleased | thrilled |
| content | joyful |
| | ecstatic |

**2** These are just a few examples to show some different shades of meaning.

a **wet**   damp, moist → soaking, saturated

b **thin**   lean, slim → bony, gaunt

c **good**   acceptable, satisfactory, reasonable → wonderful, excellent, first-rate, outstanding

d **strange**   odd, funny → bizarre, weird

## Page 23: Shades of meaning 2

**1** These are some possibilities. You may have thought of others.

a **Admire** suggests respect.

b **Demand** sounds strong, determined, angry.

c **Tossed** suggests it was without thinking or without caring.

d **Seeped** suggests it happened slowly.

e **Glowered** suggests she is angry.

f **Softly** sounds secretive, or trying not to disturb someone.

g **Hesitated** suggests they are not sure, thinking, nervous.

**2** a He **hurled** it away.

b She **hauled** it up.

c We **know** it is true.

d He **devoured** every crumb.

e I found a **shady** corner.

f They **inch** away.

## Page 24: Choosing words for effect

**1** These are some examples of words you might have used.

a Mum was **furious/livid**.

b You have **wrecked/ruined** my car.

c I **loathe/abhor/detest** salt and vinegar flavour.

d It was **extremely/highly** dangerous.

e It was a **superb/outstanding** performance.

f There was a **magnificent/breathtaking/splendid** view.

**2**  **a** He sadly **trudged** down the road.

**b** She **strolled** happily along.

**c** We nervously **paced** the room.

**d** Angrily, she **marched** down the corridor.

**e** They aimlessly **wandered** the streets.

**f** Carefully, they **stepped** onto the platform.

**3** Here is an example of a possible sentence.
A jagged slash of lightning pierced the blackness.

### Page 25: Practising synonyms and antonyms

**1**  **a** **absurd** ridiculous

**b** **elated** overjoyed

**c** **persevere** continue

**2** These are some of the most obvious possibilities.

**a** winning    **c** plentiful

**b** funny/entertaining    **d** normal/regular/usual

**3**  **a** **deserted** busy crowded

**b** **poor** wealthy prosperous

**c** **hostile** welcoming approachable

**4** These are some examples of antonyms.

**a** **shallow** deep    **d** **probable** unlikely, improbable

**b** **absent** present    **e** **partial** complete, total, whole

**c** **broad** narrow    **f** **demolish** build

**5**  **a** **antique** vase    **c** **ancient** monument    **e** **prehistoric** cave

**b** **elderly** man    **d** **outdated** clothes    **f** my **previous** school

**6**  **a** **mis**understand    **d** **un**important

**b** **in**capable    **e** **dis**orderly

**c** **im**perfect    **f** **il**legible

### Page 26: Formal and informal words 1

**1**

| | | | |
|---|---|---|---|
| **a** a rip-off | to a friend | misleading | to impress |
| **b** blew | to a friend | squandered | to impress |
| **c** very fashionable | to impress | really cool | to a friend |
| **d** woozy | to a friend | light-headed | to impress |
| **e** dehydrated | to impress | dying for a drink | to a friend |
| **f** dubious | to impress | dodgy | to a friend |

## Page 27: Formal and informal words 2

**1** These are just a few of the words you might have found in a thesaurus.

| | | | | | |
|---|---|---|---|---|---|
| a | **cheap** | inexpensive | reasonable | economical | affordable |
| b | **give** | present | donate | award | provide |
| c | **silly** | irrational | absurd | idiotic | immature |
| d | **ugly** | unattractive | unsightly | hideous | tasteless |
| e | **scary** | alarming | disturbing | shocking | frighten |
| f | **tell** | inform | advise | notify | disclose |
| g | **easy** | uncomplicated | undemanding | straightforward | manageable |
| h | **test** | examine | assess | evaluate | investigate |
| i | **ask** | enquire | request | demand | appeal |
| j | **find** | discover | locate | trace | uncover |

## Page 28: Old words

**1**

| Old words | |
|---|---|
| neckerchief | clarion |
| farthing | flagon |
| quoth | parlour |

| Newer words | |
|---|---|
| Velcro® | trainers |
| superstar | video |
| computer | rocket |

**2** These are just a few suggestions.

| | | |
|---|---|---|
| a | **writing** | scroll, parchment, runes, papyrus, scribes, fountain pen |
| b | **transport** | chariot, wagon, penny-farthing, longship, steam train |
| c | **entertainment** | hurdy-gurdy, lyre, wireless, amphitheatre |
| d | **household** | range, mangle, poker, hypocaust, carpet beater |

## Page 29: New meanings

**1**

| | | |
|---|---|---|
| a | **web** | a network of information sources accessed by the Internet |
| b | **mouse** | a handheld device that moves the cursor on a computer screen |
| c | **cookies** | data files on a computer |
| d | **text** | (verb) to send someone a message via a mobile phone |
| e | **stream** | (verb) to transfer data over the Internet |

## Page 30: Forming new nouns 1

**1**
a emoticon = **emot**ion + **icon**
b heliport = **heli**copter + air**port**
c smog = **sm**oke + f**og**
d brunch = **br**eakfast + l**unch**
e motel = **mo**tor + ho**tel**

**2**

| | | | | |
|---|---|---|---|---|
| keyboard | spreadsheet | bookmark | network | homepage |
| screensaver | laptop | firewall | backup | database |

**3**

| | | | |
|---|---|---|---|
| a multimedia | d megabyte | g multitask | j hyperlink |
| b hypertext | e hypermarket | h cybercafé | k cyberman |
| c cyber/hyperspace | f megastar | i megastore | l multimillion |

## Page 31: Forming new nouns 2

**1** **a** workaholic      **b** **shop**aholic      **c** **choc**oholic

**2** These are some possibilities. You may have found others.

     **a** **broadcast**   podcast, newscast, sportscast, webcast

     **b** **marathon**   walkathon, talkathon, spellathon, swimathon

     **c** **hardware**   software, spyware, shareware, freeware, malware

**3**

| | Original word | Shortened word |
|---|---|---|
| a | omnibus | **bus** |
| b | fanatic | **fan** |
| c | stereophonic | **stereo** |
| d | quadrangle | **quad** |
| e | limousine | **limo** |

| | Original word | Shortened word |
|---|---|---|
| f | demonstration | demo |
| g | refrigerator | fridge |
| h | electronic mail | email |
| i | application | app |
| j | advertisement | ad |

## Page 32: The origin of words 1

**1**

sphere — ball (from Greek)
opaque — shady/dark (from Latin)
equal — even/level (from Latin)
decimal — tenth (from Latin)
maximum — greatest (from Latin)
symbol — mark/token (from Greek)
minus — less (from Latin)
parallel — alongside one another (from Greek)

**2**

| | Root word | Words we use today |
|---|---|---|
| a | circle | **circle, circus** |
| b | skeletos | **skeleton, skeletal** |
| c | mobilis | **mobile, mobility** |
| d | phobos | **phobia, phobic** |
| e | digitus | **digit, digital** |
| f | vacuus | **vacuum, vacant** |

## Page 33: The origin of words 2

**1** safari      avalanche      ski      volcano

    typhoon      tsunami      pagoda      chalet

**2** **a** **pasta**   Italian      **f** **tortilla**   Spanish

     **b** **naan**   Urdu      **g** **tandoori**   Urdu

     **c** **sushi**   Japanese      **h** **spaghetti**   Italian

     **d** **croissant**   French      **i** **satsuma**   Japanese

     **e** **chilli**   Spanish      **j** **meringue**   French

# Answers continued

Page 34: Idioms

**1** **a** Too big for his boots
**b** He is bossy and arrogant (or a show-off).

**2** **a** to make a fresh start
**b** easy or simple to do
**c** all in the same (difficult) situation
**d** very happy
**e** more difficult to do than it first sounds
**f** to keep quiet
**g** to have lots of problems to worry about
**h** to not have the skills or qualities needed
**i** to trick someone or be dishonest

Page 35: Idioms and similes

**1** as cool as a cucumber — very calm, untroubled
as bright as a button — intelligent, alert, lively
like a red rag to a bull — sure to get an angry reaction
moved like lightning — very quick and sudden

**2** **a** all tangled up
**b** a scary smile
**c** soaking up ideas or knowledge.
**d** stiff and rising into peaks, not smooth.

Page 36: Onomatopoeia

**1**

| Watery sounds | Soft/quiet sounds | Loud sounds |
| --- | --- | --- |
| slosh | hum | bong |
| splash | squeak | clatter |
| splish | swoosh | crash |
| slop | swish | boom |
| plop | pitter-patter | thud |

**2** These are just a few suggestions. You might have chosen other words.
**a** splash, plop
**b** clatter, crash, bang, smash
**c** screech, clang, smash

Page 37: Using your vocabulary

**1** These are some examples, but there are many possibilities.
**a** We have numerous suggestions to consider.
**b** Please complete the form when you receive it and return it immediately.
**c** It was unfortunate that the car struck a lamppost before colliding with the lorry.

**2** **a** sprawled **b** vibrant **c** surged **d** squelched **e** flew

**3** This is just an example. You will probably have chosen different words.
Casper **rushed** forward and **grabbed** the **flaming** torch from the wall.
The **enraged** dragon **spun** round and **glared** at him. **Terrified**, Casper **frantically** waved the torch
at the **furious beast**. The dragon **raised** its head and roared **like a hundred hungry lions**.
Smoke **billowed** out of its **nostrils** and flames **shot** out of its **cavernous** mouth. The hot **blast of fiery**
breath made Casper **retreat hastily**.